You're my little puddin'.
M.T. Cobblepott

THE DAY THE PUDDING GOT AWAY

By M.T. Cobblepott

Illustrated by Yami, MT, KB and RB

Accentuate the Positive Publishing Company

Chris —
My first
in print book
I've published.
♡ Rhonda

Copyright Information

Book Design and Layout by Rhonda Bolling
Illustrations by Yami, MT and RB
FIRST EDITION

The Author, Mrs. Cobblepott

About the Author

M.T. Cobblepott lives in the woods and takes care of the forest creatures, and she has never in her life been in a pudding explosion, but she can imagine one.

Mrs. Cobblepott would like you to know that there are a few hard words in this book but we know you can learn them easily.

1. Fateful - means having an important effect on the future, and sometimes not in a good way.
2. 'Tween - is short for the word "between."
3. Confess - which means to tell or say something true.
4. Fella - is an old word and is from the word fellow, which means friend or someone you like.

M.T. Cobblepott and her publisher, Accentuate the Positive Publishing Company are donating 10% of the proceeds from the sales of this book to the Angel Fund at Island to Island Veterinary Clinic in Ketchikan, Alaska.

We hope you enjoy this fun book as much as we enjoyed preparing it for you.

Please join us for more fun on Facebook at www.facebook.com/AccentuateThePositivePublishingCompany/

or go to the website:
www.accentuatethepositivepublishing.com

They missed a pinhole in the spout.
A tiny trickle oozied out.

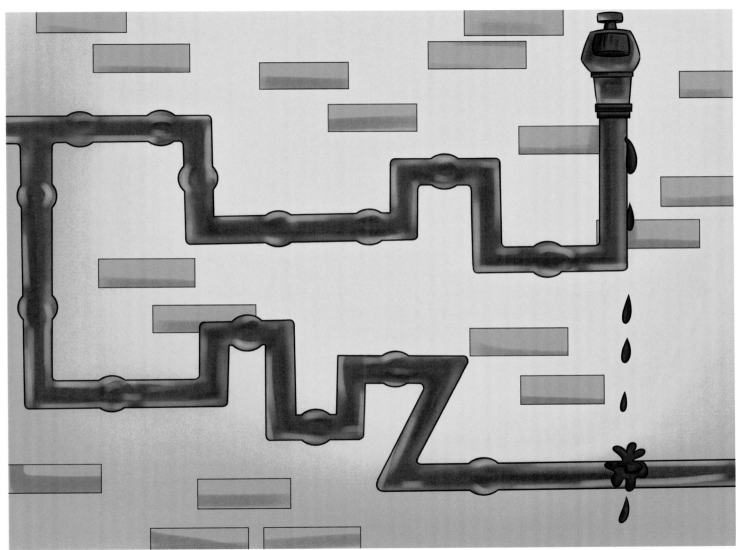

Next thing you know,
the trickle grew.

The

spigot,

spout,

and

pipes

all

BLEW!

Chocolate, chocolate in the air,
Chocolate pudding EVERYWHERE!

Chocolate on my mouth and chin,
Chocolate out and chocolate in.

Chocolate low and chocolate high,
Chocolate raining from the sky!

Chocolate here and chocolate there,
Chocolate pudding in my hair.

Chocolate in my ears and nose,
Chocolate squishing 'tween my toes.

Chocolate on the walls and floors,
Chocolate sliding down the doors.

Chocolate pudding on my face,
Chocolate, chocolate every place!

I love chocolate, I confess,
but who would want to clean this mess?

What's needed here are many hands,
and lots of chocolate pudding fans!

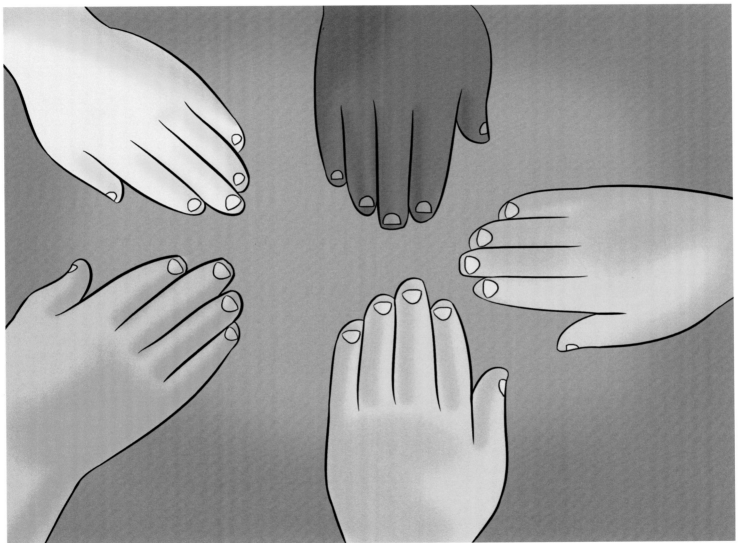

I'll call my friends and we'll all scrub,
We'll be the Chocolate Pudding Club!

Everyone can have a taste,
We can't let pudding go to waste.

The work's all done, but listen, fella,
Next time, I hope it blows vanilla!

HAVE A PUDDING PARTY AT HOME OR SCHOOL!

MRS. COBBLEPOTT'S HOMEMADE CHOCOLATE PUDDING
Pudding Club Secret Recipe

Ingredients to Serve 8

1 cup sugar

1/2 cup corn starch

6 tbsp cocoa powder, unsweetened
(secret tip: use high quality cocoa powder to vary the taste)

Chocolate chunks (semi-sweet)

1/4 tsp salt

5 1/2 cups milk

1/4 cup butter (at room temp.)
(secret tip: use Amish butter)

2 tsp vanilla extract

TOPPINGS
Whipped cream
Chocolate sprinkles (or rainbow)
Mint Leaves (if you have them)

Directions

Using a sauce pan that will hold at least 8 cups, add the sugar, corn starch, cocoa powder, and salt and stir to a smooth mixture with no lumps. Then, turn stove heat to medium and stir in the milk. Add a few small pieces of semi-sweet chocolate to melt in. Experiment! Bring to a boil, stirring constantly until your pudding is thick enough to stick to the back of a metal spoon. Go ahead and taste it after you try this (but don't burn yourself - it's hot!).

Remove from heat and stir in your butter and vanilla. Let it cool a bit. Serve in dishes or cups and add fun toppings.

Other topping ideas: Bananas, vanilla wafers, acacia seeds, almond slices, crushed candy canes, blueberries, or dried fruits, mini m&m's. Your choice.

HAVE lots of fun and send us your pictures!

Check out Mrs. Cobblepott's Facebook Page to win amazing prizes for sharing and posting your pudding party pictures and tagging Mrs. Cobblepott and AccentuateThePositivePublishingCompany. You are going to be EXCITED!